Bible Stories

from the
New Testament
rewritten especially for children

Mary is Chosen by God

Mary lived in Galilee in a town called Nazareth. She was engaged to a carpenter named Joseph. One day, an angel appeared before her.

"Do not be afraid," he told the startled girl. "God has chosen you for a very special honour. You will give birth to a son, and you are to call him Jesus. He will be God's own Son and his kingdom will never end!"

Mary was filled with wonder. "How can this be?" she asked softly. "I am not even married!"

"Everything is possible for God," replied the angel.

Mary bowed her head humbly, saying,
        "It will be as God wills it."

Born in a Manger

Now, around this time, the Emperor of Rome ordered a census. He wanted to make sure everyone paid their taxes! All the people throughout the lands ruled by Rome had to go to their hometown to be counted.

Joseph's family was descended from King David and so he and Mary had to travel to Bethlehem, where King David had been born. Mary's baby was due to be born any day, and the journey was long and hard, but they had to do as the Emperor ordered.

When Mary and Joseph finally arrived in Bethlehem, they were tired and desperately wanted to find a room for the night, for the time had come for Mary's baby to be born.

But the town was filled to bursting, for everyone had come to be counted. Every single inn was full. There was nowhere for them to stay!

At last, an innkeeper said to them, "I have no rooms free, but there is somewhere you can spend the night," and he showed them to a stable where the animals were kept. It was dirty and smelly, but it was the best they could do.

That night, Mary's baby was born. She wrapped him in strips of cloth, then laid him gently on clean straw in a manger. Mary and Joseph looked down upon their son with joy, and they named him Jesus, just as the angel had told them to.

The Shepherds on the Hillside

That same night, some shepherds were keeping watch over their flocks in the hills above Bethlehem. Suddenly the sky was filled with a blinding light!

As they fell to the ground in fear, an angel spoke to them, "Do not be afraid. I bring you good news. Today, in the town of David, a Saviour has been born to you; he is the Messiah, the Lord. Go and see for yourselves. You will find him wrapped in cloths and lying in a manger."

Then the whole sky was filled with angels praising God!

When the angels had left, the shepherds looked at one another in amazement. They could hardly believe what had just happened! But they all knew one thing – they simply had to go down to Bethlehem to see this baby with their own eyes!

The shepherds made sure that the sheep were safe, then hurried down to Bethlehem as fast as they could. They made their way to the stable, and there they found the baby lying in the manger just as they had been told. Filled with wonder and awe, the shepherds fell to their knees before the tiny baby boy who would change the world for ever.

Then they rushed off to tell everyone the wonderful news!

Following a Star

In a distant land, three wise men had been studying the stars. When they found a really bright star shining in the skies, they followed it all the way to Judea, for it was a sign that a great king had been born.

They asked King Herod in Jerusalem if he could show them the way to the baby who would be the King of the Jews. Herod was horrified! He didn't want another king around! His advisors told him of a prophecy that the new king would be born in the city of King David, in Bethlehem.

Then the cunning king sent the wise men to Bethlehem, saying, "Once you have found him, tell me where he is, so that I can visit him too!"

The wise men followed the star to Bethlehem, where they found baby Jesus in a humble house. There, they knelt before him, and presented him with fine gifts of gold, sweet-smelling frankincense, and a spicy ointment called myrrh.

Then they left to begin their long journey home – but they did not stop off at Herod's palace, for God had warned them in a dream not to tell Herod where the baby was!

Water into Wine

As the years passed, Jesus grew to be filled with grace and wisdom. God loved him, and so did everyone who knew him.

When he was grown up, Jesus and some of his friends were invited to a wedding. Everyone was having a wonderful time – until the wine ran out! Jesus' mother Mary came to tell him about the problem. She hoped he would help.

Several huge water jars stood nearby. Jesus told the servants to fill them with water, then pour the water into jugs and take them to the head waiter. When the head waiter tasted it, he was astonished. He exclaimed to the bridegroom, "You have saved the best wine till last!" for the jugs were filled with delicious wine!

This was the first of many miracles which Jesus would perform.

The Amazing Meal

A huge crowd had gathered to listen to Jesus and by evening everyone was very hungry. Jesus told his special friends, the disciples, to give them something to eat. "But Master," they replied, "there are thousands of people and we only have five loaves of bread and two fish!"

Jesus took the loaves and the fish, and looking up to heaven, broke them into pieces. He gave

them to the disciples, who took them to the people and then came back for more. He filled up the baskets again . . . and again . . . and again! There was still bread and fish left in the baskets when they came to feed the very last people! More than five thousand people were fed that day – with five loaves of bread and two fish!

Calming the Storm

Jesus and his disciples were sailing across the lake. Jesus had fallen asleep. Suddenly, the skies darkened, rain poured down and a fierce storm struck! Huge waves tossed the boat, and the disciples were terrified.

Jesus lay sleeping. The frightened disciples woke him, begging him to save them. Jesus looked up at them. "Why are you afraid? You have so little faith!" he said.

Then he stood up calmly, arms spread wide, and facing into the wind and rain, commanded, "Be still!" At once the wind and waves died down and all was calm!

The disciples were amazed. "Even the winds and waves obey him!" they said in awe.

Walking on Water

It was night and waves tossed the boat violently. Jesus had gone ashore to pray and the disciples were afraid. Then they saw a figure walking towards them on the water! They were scared until they heard the calm voice of Jesus, "It is I. Do not be afraid."

"Lord," said Simon Peter, "if it is you, tell me to come to you," and when Jesus did so, Peter put first one foot, then the other, gingerly in the water, and bravely stood up – on the water! But when he looked at the waves his courage failed him and he began to sink!

Jesus took his hand and together they walked to the boat. The wind died down and the water became calm. "Truly you are the Son of God," said the disciples.

The Sower

Many people came to listen to Jesus. He wanted them to understand his message, so he told them stories. His stories, often called parables, let people think things through for themselves. To some they would just be stories, but others would understand the real message . . .

Once Jesus told his followers a story about a farmer who sowed some seeds. The seeds all fell in different places: some fell on the path and were trampled on or eaten by birds; some fell on rocky ground where they withered because their roots could not reach the soil; some fell among weeds which choked them. Only those few that fell on good soil grew into strong, healthy plants.

Jesus was saying that he was like the farmer, and the seeds are like the message he brought from God. The seeds that fell on the path and were eaten by birds are like those people who hear the good news but pay no attention. Those on rocky ground are like people who believe for a while, but when life gets difficult they give up easily – their faith doesn't have strong roots. The seeds that fell among weeds are like those who hear, but let themselves become distracted and choked by other things.

But the seeds that fell on good soil are like those people who hear God's message and hold it in their heart. Their faith grows and grows!

The Lost Son

Jesus told a story to explain how happy God was when sinners returned to him:

"There was once a man with two sons. The younger one asked for his share of the property so he could go out into the world. He soon spent it all on enjoying himself. He ended up working for a farmer and was so hungry that sometimes he wished he could eat the food he was giving to the pigs!

"At last he came to his senses and set off home to tell his father how sorry he was. 'I'm not worthy to be his son, but maybe he will let me work on the farm,' he hoped.

"When his father saw him coming, he rushed out and threw his arms around him. The young man tried to tell him that he was not fit to be called his son, but his father told the servants to bring his finest robe for his son to wear and to kill the prize calf for a feast.

"The older son was outraged! He had worked hard for his father all this time, and nobody had ever held a feast for him! Yet here came his brother, having squandered all his money, and his father couldn't wait to kill the calf and welcome him home!

"'My son,' the father said, 'you are always with me, and all I have is yours. But celebrate with me now, for your brother was dead to me and is alive again; he was lost and is found!'"

The Good Samaritan

Once someone asked Jesus what the Law meant when it said we must love our neighbours as much as ourselves. "Who is my neighbour?" he asked. Jesus told him a story:

"A man was going from Jerusalem to Jericho, when he was attacked by robbers, who stole everything before leaving him by the road, half dead!

"Soon a priest passed by. When he saw the man, he crossed to the other side of the road and carried on his way. Then a Levite came along. He also hurried on his way without stopping.

"Nobody wanted to get involved – they were all too busy, or too important, or too scared to help!

"Now, the next person to come along was a Samaritan. The Samaritans are not friends of the Jews, but when this traveller saw the man lying by the roadside, his heart was filled with pity.

He carefully washed and bandaged his wounds, before taking him on his donkey to an inn, where he gave the innkeeper money to look after the man until he was well."

Jesus looked at the man who had posed the question, and asked who he thought had been a good neighbour to the injured man.

The man sheepishly replied, "The one who was kind to him."

Then Jesus told him, "Then go and be like him."

Thomas Doubts

That same evening, Jesus appeared to the disciples. At first, they couldn't believe it. Was he a ghost? But he spoke to them, and reassured them.

However, Thomas was not there, and when they told him about it, he couldn't believe them, saying, "Unless I put my finger where the nails were, and touch the wound in his side, I will not believe."

A week later, Jesus came among the disciples again. Turning to Thomas, he said, "Put your finger in the wounds in my hands. Reach out and feel my side. Stop doubting and believe!" Thomas was overcome with joy!

Jesus said, "You only believed because you saw me yourself. How blessed will people be who believe without even seeing!"

The Holy Spirit

Jesus had been taken up to heaven.
Before he left, he told his disciples,
"Stay here and wait for the gift that
my Father has promised you, for soon
you will be baptised with the Holy Spirit.
Then you must spread my message throughout the world."

Ten days later, the apostles were gathered together when suddenly the
house was filled with the sound of a mighty wind coming from heaven.
As they watched in wonder, tongues of fire seemed to rest on each person
there! They were all filled with the Holy Spirit, and began to speak in
different languages – ones they had never spoken before or studied!

A huge crowd gathered outside. They were amazed when the apostles came
out and began telling them all about Jesus in many different languages!

The Lame Man

A man sat begging outside the temple gates. He was lame and spent every day there, hoping for a spare coin or two. Now, as the apostles Peter and John passed by, he looked up hopefully.

Peter stopped. "I don't have any money," he said. "But I can give you something far better!"

As the lame man looked puzzled, Peter continued, "In the name of Jesus Christ, I order you to get up and walk!" and to everyone's astonishment, he helped him to stand up. The man took a cautious step, and then another, and then walked straight into the temple to gave thanks to God!

Saul Sees the Light

Saul hated all the followers of Jesus! He was prepared to stop at nothing to stamp them out and he believed that he was doing what God wanted. Many fled to Damascus. Saul set off after them, but on the way, a blinding light suddenly flashed down from above! Saul fell to the ground, covering his eyes. A voice said, "Saul, why do you keep on persecuting me?"

Saul began trembling. "Who are you, Lord?" he asked.

"I am Jesus," replied the voice. "Get up and go into the city, and you will be told what to do."

Saul struggled to his feet, but when he opened his eyes, he couldn't see a thing! His men led him into the city, where he prayed for three days without eating or drinking. Then God sent a disciple to him to lift the blindness.

Saul began to spread the good news about Jesus in the city. People were amazed. They could hardly believe it was the same man! But while his old enemies became his friends, his old friends soon became his enemies! Before long, they planned to kill him, and guarded the gates to the city so that he could not escape. But the disciples lowered him in a basket over the city walls at night!

Soon Saul began to spread the good news all across the world.

Shipwrecked

Paul was travelling on a ship to Rome, but soon found himself in the middle of a dreadful storm! For days the ship was at the mercy of the sea. The passengers and crew were filled with terror, but Paul comforted them, for God had promised that they would all reach land alive.

Everyone was thrilled when the coastline came into sight, but then the ship struck a sandbar and ran aground, and the surf began to tear the ship apart!

The centurion in charge ordered those who could swim to make for land, and told the others to cling to pieces of the wreckage and float ashore, and in this way, they reached land safely. Everyone on board was saved, just as God had promised!

Rome at Last

When Paul reached Rome, he was allowed to live by himself, with a soldier to guard him. He had many visitors, and so he carried on telling people about Jesus. He also had time to write to his friends across the world, to encourage and help them as they set up new churches.

He told them to be patient, for their suffering would make them stronger and they would find their true reward in heaven. He warned them to trust in God and not to go back to their old ways, for Christ had set them free. He urged them to live good lives, filled with love and kindness, saying, "Three things will last forever – faith, hope, and love – and the greatest of these is love!"

Before he died, he wrote, "I have fought a good fight, I have finished the race, and I have kept the faith." Paul was God's faithful servant to the end of his days.